GW00400852

# Preface

My readers may well find strange, that I can claim to be no expert on the subject of this book, but I can claim as great a fascination in stationary steam engines as anyone. My interest in steam engines has always centred on the railway locomotive, but I never let the opportunity of looking at their stationary sisters go by. An early interest in the small, often colourful, locomotives one saw from passing trains shunting in colliery yards, iron and steel works and the like, led to an early channelling of my hobby towards the industrial locomotive. It was by these means that I came to be introduced to stationary steam engines, via those magnificent colliery winding engines, very often the only clean piece of equipment one would come across at a colliery! Now a thing of the past in this country, apart from preserved examples, and despite the often greater impressiveness of the much larger pumping and mill engines, the colliery winder has a special significance for me, not only in being my introduction to the subject, but also having had the opportunity to actually sit in the engine-man's seat, and 'handle' one. Yes, not only did I sit in his seat, but together with my friend, Paul Hulme, we were trusted with the controls, and 'drove' the engine during several winds. But that's not all, for of all stationary steam engines, the colliery winder stands alone, in its flexibility of working, for it was just about the only application of large stationary steam power, where starting and stopping occurs so frequently, and where engines have such a wide range of working speeds. Generally speaking, large stationary engines run at constant speeds, or near constant speeds, for long periods; not so the colliery winder, which is constantly starting, accelerating, decelerating and stopping, as each successive wind takes place. It is an amazing sight to the uninitiated, to see a winder at work, when coal winding is in progress, and the engine is being 'pushed' to get the maximum tonnage out of the shaft. The process of 'decking', as the cage is successively stopped, so each of its floors match up with the loading and unloading platforms, enabling the tubs of coal to be loaded and unloaded, is undertaken quickly to say the least; bells ringing in the engine house to tell the engine-man when to start and stop. Equally, the engines very often exhaust direct to atmosphere, unusual for stationary engines which more normally condense, so that sounds more familiar to locomotives, are in evidence. It was also common practice, as each wind came to its end, to reverse the engine, so as to cushion the slowing down process by compression, or even apply a little 'reverse' steam.

What I failed to do, and have lived to regret, was to take more photographs of these and other engines, and many are those I watched for hours working, but took no photographs - but then, hindsight, as they say, is an exact science! But the realisation came to me in the mid 1970s, that their breed, and indeed the stationary steam engine in commercial use, was coming to the end of its life, and I set out to redress as much of the balance as I could. Therefore, I embarked on a trail of trying to see and photograph, as many of them as I could, and I travelled the length and breadth of the country doing so. Since then, the photographs and slides have, by and large, been filed away, and rarely see the light of day. Thus, when it seemed that they might be of interest to others, I jumped at the chance of putting this selection together, for otherwise they might never have emerged from the depths of the attic!

The collection is somewhat haphazard, and by no stretch of imagination does it cover even all the basic types of engine, but I have tried to give a reasonable selection of what was still about in the period I am covering, albeit many were already out of use when I saw them. It is to my lasting regret however, that I never saw any actually working, for inspiring and magnificent sight.

All enthusiasts of the stationary steam engine, and indeed anybody who would like to find out more about them, should consult the works of the late George Watkins. George, who died in January 1989, devoted his entire life to the study of the stationary steam engine, and went to great lengths, despite the rather primitive equipment in his early days, to take a collection of exceptional photographs of most of what he saw, and they form a collection second to none. His series of books, which are listed later, are a must for all interested in the subject, and treasured volumes in my own library. We are indeed grateful to George, for without his foresight over many years, there is absolutely no doubt, our knowledge of the subject would be far less than it is. He was very much on his own in those days, for almost nobody else troubled to visit, study, photograph and record, those masterpieces of British engineering, which were so beautifully cared for.

I have enjoyed immensely, putting this collection together, and I am grateful to Allan Condie, for his confidence in publishing it. If it proves successful, then maybe he will be persuaded to commission a sequel; for I have more then enough material to fill another volume this size! If my readers find some enjoyment in the pages that follow, or find an 'old' friend hiding away between these covers, I shall be content, that my efforts have not gone unrewarded. Except for one, duly credited, all the photographs are of my own taking, and for those who take an interest in such subjects, I use 'Pentax' screw thread, 35 m/m cameras, and FP4 film. Of course, most of the shots employed a wide angle lens and a tripod, being time exposures. Any errors a diligent reader might detect are of course, my own responsibility, but I shall be glad to hear of them, so that any possible subsequent volume, might contain the necessary corrodents.

In concluding these few remarks, I would like to thank all the many people who have helped me on my visits. I was always treated with the utmost courtesy by owners and guides alike, and rarely were visits refused. The National Coal Board are deserved of special mention here, if only by shear weight of the numbers of engines they owned; but everybody was so helpful. No effort was too great to enable me to get the best possible photograph, and all number of 'things' had to be moved in this quest! Although not illustrated in this book - readers will have to wait and see if Volume Two ever arrives - I well recall my visit to Askern Main Colliery, near Doncaster. This colliery had two of the three largest winding engines ever used in this country, and my visit coincided with the last week of working for one of them, on the eve of its replacement by an electric motor. After taking my photographs, I had a lengthy chat with its 'driver', and before long this gentleman was reduced to tears; on the following Saturday he would handle 'his' engine for the last time, and after the annual holidays he would 'go electric'. There was no doubt that this 'guy' did not enjoy his holidays that year, and when I left him, he was completely broken down with emotion, for over the years, he had become so attached to 'his' engine. What better epitaph can the magnificent engines in the pages that follow have, for they are indeed masterpieces, one and all, and we are all the worse for their demise. I salute the stationary steam engine in all its forms, and I look back on my visits with immense gratitude, that I was able to see as much as I did.

I commend any of my readers who find interest in this book, to go along and visit some of the engines that have been so beautifully preserved and restored, and we are all grateful to those who tender them. Doubtless the 'bug' will soon hit him, as it did me, but any engine in preservation cannot capture the atmosphere of the engines in their true working environment, more's the pity.

Last, but by no means least, as ever with my books, many thanks to my wife, Angela, for all her help and assistance, not only in general support, but for proof reading and the final preparation of this draft for the publisher.

Also to Kevin, who saw so little of his 'Dad' while he was locked away in his study almost day and night.

Allan C Baker
Copper Beeches
Llanvaches
Gwent

February 1990

# Introduction

The steam engine as much as, if not more than anything else, was responsible for the tremendous industrial development of this country, and subsequently the world. To Thomas Newcomen (1663-1729), goes the credit for first successfully, applying steam power to drive an engine to do useful work, although there are some who would disagree with this statement, in its strictest sense. Newcomen developed an engine with an up and down motion, which could be used for pumping purposes, although his engine should more properly be described as an atmospheric engine, as it employed atmospheric pressure, albeit the vacuum on the opposite side of the piston, was created by steam, to actually move the piston in the cylinder. But the principle of a piston moving in a cylinder was established. Engines of this type, were widely used for mine pumping purposes, not only all over this country, but later in many other parts of the world.

It was James Watt (1691-1782), who by increasing the pressure of the steam, made the cycle a true steam cycle, in that steam pressure actually forced the piston, rather than it moving by atmospheric pressure due to a vacuum being created on one side of it. Later, by means of his 'sun and planet' motion, he made the engine rotative; that is it turned a wheel, and this invention, necessary to circumvent existing patents, used a series of gearwheels to transmit the up and down motion of the piston, to a flywheel. Later still, this was replaced by the straightforward crank, as we know it today. Subsequent to this, he introduced the principle of a double acting engine, ie., steam was used to push the piston in both directions; hitherto, the return stroke was completely unproductive. In effect, this double acting arrangement, doubled the power output for any given size of engine.

All these engines were beam engines, and the motion between cylinder and pump rod, or crank, was transmitted by an overhead beam, with a centre pivot. Engines of this principle remained in production well into the present century, although their popularity declined. Indeed, developments by various Cornish Engineers, perfected what became known as the Cornish Beam Engine, and engines of this type, which found most, but not all their employment in that county, were non rotative, and were used almost exclusively, for mine pumping. They came in enormous sizes, cylinders up to and exceeding 100" diameter, and because such large cylinders enabled steam pressures to be kept low, boiler maintenance was exceptionally light, and longevity almost limitless - hence, many of them were still operative well into the present century, and some even after the last war.

Over the succeeding years, there have been other developments to the beam engine, including compounding - some engines being converted to compound several years after initial construction. Most of the early examples were 'house built'; that is, the house they were in, provided the framework on which the various components were mounted. The 'Woolf' compound employed cylinders side by side, on the same end of the beam, whilst the 'Mc Naught', had cylinders on each side of the beam. Beam pivots were in differing places, and engines built to be self standing - for example, with an 'A' frame beam pivot, a single column, or four column beam support arrangement, and several other types. Fortunately, examples of most types have survived into preservation, many of them still in their original surroundings.

The fear by the early designers and builders, that wear and tear on the cylinder if it was placed horizontally, would prove prohibitive, was largely demolished by the introduction of such an arrangement on the early railway locomotives, forced on their designers by practical considerations. So the stationary engine builders soon followed suit, and development of horizontal engines went on apace. All number of shapes and sizes were used, compounding coming early; ie, the use of steams expansive properties, firstly at high pressure in a comparatively small cylinder, and then after exhausting into a receiver, expanding it further, at a lower pressure, and in a larger cylinder. Use of different sized cylinders, led to equal, or near equal power from both, and an evening of torque. By this double use of the steam, obvious economy in steam production was effected, aided and abetted by improvements in boiler design and construction, leading to higher pressures, and therefore, greater opportunities for expansion of the steam. Further developments, including triple and even quadruple expansion of the steam followed. Care however, had to be taken to ensure that the last cylinder in the cycle still exhausted at a positive pressure, and to assist this, condensers were designed to create a vacuum in the low pressure exhaust receiver. This ensured that even if the steam was fully expanded in the low pressure cylinder, it could still exhaust freely, and not create back pressure.

Sometimes the cylinders were placed side by side, known as cross-compounds, on in line, known as tandems compounds. As triple expansion engines were introduced, the three cylinders were sometimes placed in line, or side by side, frequently with two low pressure cylinders (ie, four cylinders in all), the high pressure cylinder being in tandem with a low pressure one on one side of the engine, and the intermediate pressure cylinder in tandem with another low pressure cylinder, on the other side.

Obviously, as these developments were underway, improvements took place in the steam distribution and governing arrangements. The simple slide valve and link motion, was augmented by more sophisticated and efficient piston valves, and later the 'Drop' and 'Corliss' valves were introduced. The latter was invented by an American, George Corliss, in 1849, and the principle consisted of separate valves for inlet and exhaust, and at both ends of the cylinders, thus allowing for differing openings in all positions. Consisting of circular bobbin type valves, moving in the opposite plain to conventional piston valves, ie., at right angles to the cylinder bore, their great advantage was the small size needed for the working chambers, enabling them to be placed close to the ends of the cylinder, resulting in much reduced clearance volumes. They also allowed for a wide opening of the inlet port during steam admission, reducing wire drawing of the steam. The use of separate valves for both inlet and exhaust, eliminated successive heating and cooling of the steam passages too, increasing the efficiency as a result.

The 'Drop' valve had somewhat similar attributes, and use of a trip mechanism, with both types, enabled the admission of the steam to be controlled by direct linkage from the governor, so that link motion, with all its attendant problems of wear and tear, could be dispensed with; it had of course, no other function to perform on many stationary steam engines, as in a lot of installations there was no need for them to be capable of reversing. The 'Meyer' slide valve was another method of altering the cut-off of the steam admission, without the need for link motion, and this used what was in effect, a second slide valve, operating on the back of the conventional slide valve, and controlling ports within the body of the normal valve. This allowed the cut-off to be altered irrespective of the travel of the conventional valve. Engines were built with all sorts of combinations of valves, and an engine might, for example, have 'Corliss' inlet and piston exhaust valves, thus employing the advantages of the different types where they were most suitable.

Vertical engines became popular for some applications, especially where floor space was at a premium. Sometimes the cylinders were at the bottom of the crank, others, more popular, had the cylinders above, ie., inverted, and the crank was below. This type was particularly popular in triple expansion configuration for water pumping and, due to its potential high power output, and small floor space, almost universal in ships.

The last real development of the stationary steam engine was the Uniflow, which could truly be considered the ultimate in terms of thermal efficiency. It was designed by a German, Dr Johann Stumpf, in 1908, and in the design, the steam was admitted at both ends of the cylinder, as in the double acting arrangement, but exhausted via ports in the cylinder wall, at mid stroke - the ports being similar to those in a two stroke diesel. By these means, inlet and exhaust ports, together with the complete sections of the cylinder, were used by either inlet or exhaust steam, but not both, and therefore, they were not subjected to rapid changes of temperature, hence the large increase in thermal efficiency.

However, this invention did not stem the tide to any great extent, and apart from the steam turbine, developments in the design and construction of steam power came to an end with the Uniflow. Improvements there were, but to all intents and purposes, the systematic development of the stationary steam engine came to an end with the First World War, after over two hundred years, and although they remained in construction, in ever decreasing numbers, until the 1950s, they were a dying breed.

Many were the builders of stationary steam engines in this country, they were found all over the place, although, as would be expected, they were more concentrated in the industrial areas. Most builders tended to specialise in particular types of engine, like colliery winding engines, mill engines, water pumping engines etc., but generally they would turn their hands to anything. For example, Worsley Mesnes of Wigan, and Markham of Chesterfield, not only specialised in winders, but became almost synonymous with them, whilst Hawthorn Davey of Leeds, gained a similar reputation for pumping engines. Likewise, Buckley & Taylor of Oldham, and John Musgrave of Bolton, specialised in textile mill engines. However, firms like Robey's of Lincoln, and Marshall's of Gainsborough, were more versatile, and built engines to a great variety of designs and sizes, and again we are lucky, that examples of most builders work survive in preservation.

## Recommended Reading:-

Allen JS, and Rolt LTC, The Steam Engine of Thomas Newcomen, Moorland Publishing 1977.

Barton DB, The Cornish Steam Engine, D Bradford Barton Ltd., 1965.

Bowden C, Cooper G, and McAvoy T, Stationary Steam Engines in Great Britain - A Check List, Colin Bowden 1979.

Buchanan RA, and Watkins G, The Industrial Archaeology of the Steam Engine, Allen Lane 1976.

Dickinson HW, and Jenkins R, James Watt & The Steam Engine, Moorland Publishing 1981 (reprint of 1st Edition 1927).

Hayes G, A Guide to Stationary Steam Engines, Moorland Publishing 1981.

Watkins George, The Stationary Steam Engine, David & Charles 1968

The Textile Mill Engine, two volumes, David & Charles, Vol 1 1971; Vol 2 1971.

The Steam Engine In Industry, two volumes, Moorland Publishing; Vol 1 1987; Vol 2 1979

Woodall FD, Steam Engines & Water Wheels, Moorland Publishing 1975.

1. Sherwood Colliery at Mansfield Woodhouse in Nottinghamshire, had two steam winders until the early 1980s, both built by Frazer & Chalmers of Erith, (later part of GEC) in 1903. This view shows the No 1 downcast shaft engine, a 2800 bhp cross-compound, the shaft being 446 yards deep and the engine adapted to haul skips rather than conventional cages, each skip with a man riding deck. The pay load was 6 tons 10 cwt per skip, with a rope speed of 62 ft per sec when coal winding; 30 ft per sec with men. At the time this photograph was taken on 21 June 1980, the engine was lifting between 19000 and 20000 tons per week, and on conversion of the shaft to skip winding it had been slowed down, and the dashpots fitted to the 'Corliss' valves - both inlet and exhaust - were no longer in use. The cylinders were 32" and 53" with a 5'6" stroke, the working pressure being 150 psi. As I watched the engine wind, the low pressure receiver pressure registered 50 psi.

2. The No 2 shaft engine was similar, but a duplex of 1901, with a parallel drum and conventional cages; the No 1 engine had a by-conical drum to ease the load on the engine at the commencement of each wind. Notice the smaller sized cylinder, enclosed drum, 'Corliss' valves for both inlet and exhaust, and the steam reversing gear. Frazer & Chalmers were renowned for the excellence of their engines, and they made a number of colliery winders for this country, but compound winders were relatively rare, and even then only used for the deeper shafts.

3. *Robey of Lincoln, built some very efficient and neat winders, and this is the right hand cylinder of the downcast engine at Westhorpe Colliery, at Heath in Derbyshire, on 21 June 1980. This was a duplex engine, with 'The Robey Patent Drop Valve Gear', built in 1924. This gear enabled one eccentric to operate both inlet and exhaust valves, at each end of the cylinder, and in both forward and reverse. The shaft at Westhorpe was 144 yards deep (the upcast was a drift), and the engine had cylinders 22"x40", with a 12' drum, winding 3 tons 14 cwt per run at 40 ft per second - around 10000 tons per week being lifted this way. Notice the makers number on the cylinder. Robey treated their winders as two separate engines, both sides having separate numbers, in this case 40223 for the right hand, and 40224 for the left hand.*

4-5-6. *Three illustrations, also taken on 21 June 1980, of the splendid old Lilleshall duplex winder dating from 1902, at the north, downcast shaft of Pleasley Colliery in Derbyshire, by this time used for man riding, and materials only. Notice the engine is fitted with 'Cornish' valves, both inlet and exhaust, driven by link motion; the engine finished work, and was scrapped, about one year later. The Lilleshall Company of Oakengates in Shropshire, although prolific builders of stationary steam engines, did not build many colliery winders.*

5. *See caption 4 for details.*

6. *See caption 4 for details.*

7. This is the other engine at Pleasley, at the southern, upcast shaft, taken on the same date, a 'standard' Markham of Chesterfield, duplex machine, built in 1923. Cylinders were 36"x84", working at 150 psi, and fitted with drop inlet valves, and 'Corliss' exhaust, driven by link motion and wrist plates. The shaft was 1000 yards deep, the winding depth being 870 yards, and all the coal was normally drawn via this shaft, each run having a maximum pay load of 7.3 tons. Both engines were fed by a battery of nine 'Lancashire' boilers, six being in steam at any one time, and they all dated from 1927. Pleasley Colliery had an extremely neat layout, the two winders being back to back, in adjoining engine houses.

8. Another duplex Markham winder was at Orgreave Colliery near Sheffield, cylinders were 39"x66", built in 1926, it was fitted with drop inlet valves, but on this occasion piston exhaust - not a common arrangement. The shaft was 1200 ft deep, and five ton capacity skips had replaced the cages in August 1966; the engine had a full speed of 69 rpm with an 18' diameter parallel drum. The illustration shows the drivers eye view, notice the throttle and reversing controls, the brakes were foot operated, the dial showing the position of the skips in the shaft. Your author had the immense pleasure of driving this engine, the only one he has ever 'handled', and his colleague Paul Hulme, standing alongside, gives some idea of the size of the engine. It was beautifully kept when this photograph was taken on 27 September 1980, but finished work the following year, and wound its last coal on 12 October 1981.

9. *John Warner of Hanley, Stoke-on-Trent, was a little known builder, especially outside North Staffordshire, who nevertheless, made extremely robust and trouble-free machines. This is one of his few winders outside North Staffordshire, the upcast shaft engine at Bentinick Colliery, near Kirkby-in-Ashfield in Nottinghamshire, a duplex engine built in 1890, with cylinders 36" x 60"; this would be one of Warner's biggest engines, and the photograph was taken on 8 April 1980. Notice the driving position on the right, the normal winding speed being but 25 rpm, and the working pressure 100 psi. Local legend had it that the engine came second hand in 1915, having previously been at Brodsworth Colliery in Yorkshire; it ceased work in 1978. However, because its house was integral with the boiler house, and because the boilers were still in use, it survived. This was an old engine in design principles, with slide valves, and few other refinements, hence its slow winding speed, but it excellent construction was evident.*

10. *Builders plate of the Warner engine.*

11-12. These two illustrations show the No 1 upcast winder at Bickenshaw Colliery, Leigh in Lancashire, built in 1875 by John Wood & Sons Limited, of Wigan. A duplex engine with 36"x72" cylinders, notice the link motion, drop inlet valves and slide exhaust, an unusual combination; notice too, the massive construction. This was a large engine by a builder whose products were generally confined to his 'home' county, but its age is given away by many of its design features. In later practice, the separate slide bars generally gave way to a cast trunk guide, which was far easier to construct - being castings - and of course, minimised the time and skill needed to properly set up separate bars, and keep them in adjustment. Notice the governor, overwind control to the extreme right of plate 12, parallel drum and steam reverser. It was usual to have servo control for both reverser and brakes on winders, to ease the manual effort of driving them, with the constant starting and stopping, the frequency of which was almost unique among stationary steam engines. When these photographs were taken on 1 March 1979, the engine was on stand-by only, for emergency man riding, and it was scrapped a couple of years later.

13. Another of Robey's neat duplex engines (No 40516 right hand; No 40517 left hand), built in 1922, fitted with 36"x48" cylinders, and installed at the No 1 upcast shaft of Linby Colliery, near Hucknell in Nottinghamshire. The working level was 226 yards, but when the engine was installed in 1924, it wound from 440 yards. This illustration shows well the 'Patent' valve gear, see plate 3, which made the engines very light to handle, hence they were fast, and did not usually require servo assistance for reversing.

15. *Builders plate of the left hand engine in Plate 14.*

14. *This is the other, downcast winder at Linby, a smaller Robey (No 40542 left hand: No 40453 right hand), built in 1926, but not installed over the 226 yard deep shaft, until two years later. Cylinders in this case were 24"x40", working pressure 100 psi, and winding speed 45 ft per second, the drum was 14' diameter, and the pay load 4.6 tons per wind. To illustrate the flexibility of these extremely neat Lincolnshire built engines, this one averaged 78 runs per hour, and had been known to average 84 runs for long periods, when pressed, and this equated to 386 tons of coal lifted every hour. These photographs were taken on 16 August 1980, and show well the beautiful condition the engines were kept in.*

16. *On 28 August 1980, Donnisthorpe Colliery in Leicestershire, still operated this very neat duplex winder, built by J Jessop of Leicester, at an unknown date, but without doubt in the last century. It had been rebuilt by Messrs Worsley Mesnes of Wigan, their number 13311F. Fitted with Allen straight link motion and steam reverse, the piston valves were unusual for such an application, and doubtless Worsley Mesnes, fitted new cylinders and valves during the rebuild. The cylinders themselves were approximately 24"x54", and the working pressure was 80 psi - normal speed 35 rpm. By the time this photograph was taken the engine, which wound the upcast shaft, was used for men and materials only, all the coal being wound at nearby Rawdon Colliery, the two pits having had their underground workings connected.*

17. *Builders plate of the engine illustrated in Plate 16.*

18. *So far as I am aware, this engine was almost unique, notice the valve gear and 'tumbler' reverse, ie, the large right angle drive gearbox visible to the left, on the valve operating shaft. This box moved bodily through around 30%, to move the eccentric shaft, thus reversing the engine. Built by Galloways of Manchester, a firm better known for its mill engines, it had been installed at the No 1 upcast shaft of Parsonage Colliery, near Leigh in Lancashire in 1923. A duplex machine with 40"x72" cylinders, and drop valves, it was very probably the only winder built by this firm. The 17' diameter drum was parallel, and by the time I took this picture on 8 December 1977, the colliery had ceased coal winding, all the coal being drawn via connected underground workings at nearby Bickenshaw, so its sole traffic was men and materials. As is obvious, the engine was in immaculate condition, and well cared for by its drivers and maintenance staff; alas, it did not long survive this photograph.*

19. *Thornewill & Warham of Burton-on-Trent are, perhaps, better known for their association with the brewers of that town, then with colliery winding engines, but nevertheless, they built some fine examples. This is the 1868 built upcast engine at Cadley Hill Colliery, at Church Cresley in Derbyshire, taken on 28 August 1980. The engine was a duplex, with 24"x48" cylinders, simple slide valves and link motion, interestingly, driven by a separate small crank, outboard of the main crank. Like the Donnisthorpe engine, plate 16, it had been rebuilt by Worsley Mesnes of Wigan, and according to its driver, had originally been an underground haulage engine at nearby Brethy No 1 Colliery - it seems a little large to me for such purpose though. Despite its age, it was in excellent condition, well looked after, albeit somewhat out of place, at this otherwise fully modernised colliery.*

20-21. When I took these two photographs on 28 August 1980, Walton Colliery in Yorkshire, had already ceased coal winding, but it was still a fantastic place; indeed it had to all intents and purposes been 'mothballed' for several years, but at the time of my visit, closure operations were underway. As well as two steam winders, there were steam compressors, a steam fan engine, and steam generating plant, both reciprocating and turbine. This is the No 1 upcast winder, (shaft depth 585 yards) built in 1880 by John Fowler of Leeds, a builder who sent most of his products abroad, and brought to Walton in 1906, from an earlier user in South Wales. A duplex machine with expansion link motion driving piston valves, it was still in use winding men and materials, as the clearance operations were still underway. Notice the massive bed, the drivers position, the reversing engine cylinder - horizontal and just in front of the controls - along with the parallel drum, and hydraulic brake. Unfortunately, by this time the engine was extremely woebegone and unkempt, but it was nevertheless, a fine example of a large 19th century winder.

22. *Another of the relatively unusual cross compound winders was at Bank Hall Colliery, near Burnley in Lancashire, on this occasion built by the local firm of Worsley Mesnes in Wigan. This is the left hand, low pressure cylinder, with drop inlet valves and 'Corliss' exhaust, driven via link motion and wrist plates - notice the piston tail rod, to help take the weight of the large low pressure piston. Taken on 28 May 1971, the engine finished work a matter of weeks later.*

23. *Another common use of steam power at collieries, was for compressed air, and this view shows the twin cross compound compressors at Chatterley Whitfield Colliery, near Tunstall in Stoke-on-Trent, on 21 November 1970. Built by Walker Brothers of Wigan, prolific builders of such engines, the air cylinders were behind the steam cylinders, and just off the picture to the left. These engines were of course, non reversing, and 'Corliss' valves were used for both inlet and exhaust, the engines running at constant speed for weeks on end. Notice on the raised level to the rear of the engines, a turbine, and this also drove a compressor, and ran on the low pressure exhaust from the reciprocating engines. When this photograph was taken the engines were already out of use, and they were scrapped shortly after.*

24-25. *This was the smaller of two, cross compound Walker Brothers compressors at Sutton Manor Colliery, St Helens in Lancashire, and built in 1912. Notice the air cylinders to rear of the steam cylinders; it could deliver 5000 cub ft of air per minute, and was scrapped in 1979, after an accident - when a crosshead cotter came adrift from the crosshead, and the associated cylinders, both steam and air, were smashed. Photograph taken on 1 September 1978. Together with a larger sister engine, it exhausted into a low pressure turbine, itself driving a 2000 kwa alternator, which supplied electricity to the colliery.*

26. As with their compressors, Walker Brothers were well known for their fan engines, used for mine ventilating. This is the small fan engine at Bank Hall Colliery near Burnley, photograph taken on 22 May 1971. A single cylinder example with 'Corliss' valves, notice the rope drive - quite usual for such applications - although but three ropes seem sufficient to drive the fan, which would be enclosed at the top of the downcast shaft, itself behind the wall to the rear. When this photograph was taken, the engine was on stand-by only, electric fans having superseded it for normal use. A nice example of the small steam engines found around most collieries for similar purposes.

27. An example of the type of engine much used around collieries, both above and below ground, and for all sorts of purposes, from shaft sinking to underground haulage, is this one at Silverdale Colliery, near Newcastle-under-Lyme in Staffordshire, photographed on 12 July 1980. Built locally by John Warner of Hanley - see plate 9 - a duplex engine, with cylinders 12"x22", it was in occasional use for cleaning the rising main water pipes in the No 16 upcast shaft, which was only in use for ventilation and pumping by this date. Notice the reduction gear drive to the drum, reversing link motion and flywheel. This engine would, in all probability, have started life as an underground haulage engine, and it would date from the latter part of the 19th, or early 20th century.

28. *Passing now from colliery winding to textile mill engines, another industry in which stationary steam engines were in great demand. All of those architectural wonderful mill buildings, that are so much a part of the Lancashire and West Yorkshire landscape, were once powered by steam, and the empty engine house, can usually be identified, generally an integral part of the main building. Few however, still contain these magnificent engines, for it was in the textile mill environment, that the stationary steam engine perhaps, reached it peak in both power and magnificence. This is the cross compound engine of Leigh Spinners Limited, at their mill in Leigh, Lancashire, photographed on 1 September 1980. A beautiful piece of machinery, it was built by Yates & Thom of Blackburn in 1925, who were perhaps, the most prolific and well known of the Lancashire builders, and here is one of the last engines they made. Cylinders sizes are: high pressure 36", and seen on the left, and low pressure 60", to the right, the stroke being 5'; notice each side of the engine carries a name, 'Mayor' and 'Mayoress'. 'Corliss' valves are used for both inlet and exhaust, and unlike colliery winders, the valve gear is simple, the engine of course, being none reversing. 'Mayor' and 'Mayoress', generated 2000 bhp, and by the time this photograph was taken, the mill had been converted to individual electric drives for the looms, but the engine had been connected, via an 11 rope drive, to an electric alternator, of 500 kva capacity, thus becoming the stand-by power plant for the mill. To turn the alternator at 325 rpm, giving a 50 cycle output, the engine ran at 60 rpm, and had last been used for such purpose, some three years previously, although steam was available all the time, and the engine, and its room, were both warm and clean. Most fortunately, this engine has been retained in situ, and access is available by appointment.*

29. *Makers plate of the engine in Plates 30 and 31.*

30-31. Mary' (it was quite common to name mill engines), is a nice example of a smaller tandem compound engine - ie, cylinders in line with each other - built by S S Stott & Company Limited, of Haslingdon Lancashire, in 1895, and photographed on 24 April 1980, at the Baiting Mill, at Norden, near Rochdale, of Cudworth Bros (Norden) Ltd. The high pressure cylinder was 12", the low pressure 24", and the stroke 36". 'Corliss' valves on the high pressure, and slide on the low. Like the engine at Leigh - plate 28 - the direct drive to the looms had been replaced by individual electric motors, and the engine converted to drive an alternator for stand-by power, in this case an old BTH machine giving an output of 400 volts at 452 amps, 3 phase, 50 cycles, and via a traditional rope drive. The engine had last been used for such purposes during the infamous 'three day week', of the 'Heath' Government. The 'locals' claimed the high pressure cylinder had been added some years after the engine was installed, to increase its power, but I felt this unlikely.

32. *A very neat example of a smaller, and indeed much older, cross compound built by Ashton Frost & Company, also of Blackburn, in 1884. High pressure cylinder was 17", and fitted with 'Corliss' valves, low pressure cylinder 36 1/2", and fitted with slide valves. The engine ran at 42 rpm, on 80 psi steam pressure, and was rated at 350 bhp. When I took this photograph on 24 April 1980, at the Indian & Primrose Mill in Church, near Accrington, of Edger Davies Limited, the engine was stopped for lunch, and had but two months left to run. At this time but 200 of the mill's looms were still driven by the line shafting; there had been over 1000, gradual replacement by individual electric motors being well underway. The engine was nevertheless, in lovely condition, in a very pleasing shade of maroon, and when we arrived at the mill just before lunch, we were able to witness the engineer going through the process of stopping it. How absorbing the see him take control of the engine manually from the governor, and gradually ease the steam off, while the looms were unloaded one by one, as the staff left for lunch. Equally, after an extremely pleasant hour, we were able to see the same process in reverse, as the looms came on stream, and the governor was able to take over - once this was so, the engineer retired to attend to the boiler! The large square looking object just behind the low pressure cylinder to the right, is the condenser vacuum pump, driven off the piston tail rod. Few mills were still steam operated when this picture was taken, but the memories of that day will linger on for all time.*

34. *See caption 35 for details.*

33. *Makers plate of the Ashton Frost engine in Plate 32.*

34-35-36. *Another small tandem compound, with the cylinders reversed from the previous engine, ie, the high pressure is behind the low pressure, their dimensions being 16" and 32", with a 48" stroke. Built by William Roberts & Sons, of Nelson Lancashire, in 1895. 'Peace' is seen here at the Queen Street Manufacturing Company Limited, a cotton weaving mill at Harle Syke, near Briercliffe in Lancashire, on 13 March 1980. Running speed was 70 rpm, working pressure 100 psi, and bhp 500; this was a single floor mill, with line shafting. All the valves were of the 'Corliss' type, and plate 36 illustrates well their operating gear, with the trip mechanism and dash pots, the latter to ensure 'sharp', dampened operation of the valves. Another beautifully kept engine, one could literally eat ones food off both the engine and the engine room floor; it was a pleasure to correspond with the engineer afterwards, and send him copies of these, and other photographs taken on the visit. The boiler plant consisted of two 'Lancashire' boilers, by Tinker Shenton of Hyde, mechanically fed on Bickenshaw 'singles', the consumption being 3 1/2 tons per day - there was a 'Greens' economiser too.*

37. An interesting view, showing well the 'Corliss' valves, operating gear and wrist plates, on a horizontal single cylinder Pollit & Wigzell of Sowerby Bridge engine, built in 1923, and powering a brick works. Photographed on 29 March 1980, the engine was at the works of Roberts & Maginnis Limited, silica brick manufacturers at Trevor, near Ruabon. This works had supplied bricks for lining the open hearth steel furnaces at Hawarden Bridge Steel Works, near Shotton in Flintshire, but when that plant ceased steel making, so did the brick works close too, only a few weeks before this photograph was taken. Notice the large flywheel, rope drive, and the spare piston rings in the left foreground.

38. To illustrate the once numerous high speed vertical enclosed engines, I have chosen this view of one of the three generating sets at the New Cheshire Salt Works Limited, at Wincham in Cheshire, taken on 2 August 1980. This two cylinder compound piston valve engine, was built by Belliss & Morcom Limited, of Birmingham in 1937, a company that was as much responsible as anybody, for the development of this type of steam engine, and its success. The engine seen here was Belliss No 9430, running at 375 rpm on 150 psi steam pressure, and directly coupled to a 437.5 kva three phase alternator, with a separate exciter; with two sets on load at any one time, these engines could supply the entire electrical load for the works.

39-40. The next subject is that of water pumping, one of the last commercial uses of stationary steam power in this country. Here we see one of two extremely tidy, horizontal cross compounds, at Wadden Pumping Station, of The Thames Water Authority, near Croydon, on 11 August 1980. The engines were built by James Simpson & Company Limited - later Worthington Simpson - in 1910 and 1915, and the first illustration shows the low pressure cylinder of the 1915 engine. Valves were 'Meyer' expansion slide, and the cylinders 24" and 42", with a 60" stroke, the engines running at 16 rpm, on 100 psi working pressure, and rated at 120 bhp. The valve gear consists of two valves per cylinder, allowing for expansive working by varying the cut off, without the use of 'normal' link motion, unnecessary otherwise, as there was no requirement for the engines to reverse; normally only the high pressure valves were so adjusted. The twin eccentrics of this expansion gear can be seen on Plate 40, as can the 'V' form barring engine. Steam barring engines were found on most stationary engines, both to assist starting, and for maintenance purposes. There were two sets of pumps, usual practice with water pumping engines, a set of force pumps being driven from the high pressure piston tail rods, which forced the water to nearby Russell Hill reservoir. The other set were the well lift pumps, driven off the low pressure piston tail rods, and they lifted the water from the underground well. One engine was in use at any one time, on a five week cycle, and amazingly, steam was still generated by a battery of three, hand fired, single flue 'Cornish' boilers, one being in steam at any one time, except for the rare occasions when it was necessary to run both engines, in which case two boilers were steamed. Typical of all pumping stations, as can been seen, the environment was spotless.

41. *Inverted triple expansion engines were popular for water pumping, and in them the industry probably reached its peak of efficiency with steam power. This is one of two engines installed at Maple Brook - the No 1 engine - near Lichfield in Staffordshire, and built by W & J Galloway of Manchester in 1913. Cylinders were 22", 35" and 55", with a 48" stroke, 'Corliss' valves being used in all positions; observe the twin flywheels. Superheated steam at 160 psi was supplied from three 'Lancashire' boilers, also by Galloway. Notice too, the pumps driven from the extra cranks outboard of each flywheel; these are the bore hole lift pumps, each 5" by 60". The force pumps, to deliver the water to Gentleshaw Reservoir, were three in number, one to each cylinder, and driven by the twin rods seen attached to each crosshead; they were 13 1/2"x48". Over 24 hours this engine could lift and deliver 2,000,000 gallons from the 300' level of the 632' deep bore holes, and with a head of 306' on the force pumps. Notice the engine is named, the plates 'H Ashton Hill', being mounted between the low and intermediate pressure cylinders; Hill was a Director of the South Staffordshire Water Company. Although I took this picture on 4 October 1980, long after the engine finished work, I did see both it, and its scrapped sister (this was similar, but built by Glenfield & Kennedy of Kilmarnock in 1921), working in 1971; the No 1 engine steamed for the last time on 5 April 1972, the No 2 engine late the previous year.*

42-43. *Hawthorn Davey & Company of Leeds, were well known for their pumping engines, and made a speciality of tandem compound horizontal machines like this one, at Brindley Bank Pumping Station of the South Staffordshire Water Company, and dating from 1907. Cylinders were 36"x72" with a 72" stroke; 'Meyer' expansion slide valves and a double web crank were other features. The force pumps were driven off the piston tail rod, and the well pumps, as can be seen in Plate 43, from the main crankpin - hence the twin webs. Notice too, in this illustration the small winch engine, used for maintenance purposes in the well shaft. The engine was photographed on 4 October 1980, but had finished work in 1968, and is now preserved on site. For many years in charge of the Bradbury family, I have spent many happy hours watching it go effortlessly about its business, at a steady 20 rpm. Unusually, there was but one engine on this site, and it normally only pumped on a day shift, so one could have the added pleasure of seeing the starting and stopping operation every day, an absorbing procedure.*

44-45. *The 'Cornish' none reciprocating beam engine, was extremely popular for pumping purposes, being in almost sole command for such purposes in its 'home' county, until well into the present century. This example however, was photographed at the Sandfields Pumping Station of the South Staffordshire Water Company, at Lichfield on 1 October 1980. Built by Jonah & George Davies of Tipton in 1873, it has a single cylinder 65"x108" stroke, and worked at 40 psi steam pressure, giving 150 bhp at its normal seven strokes per minute. This engine supplemented three James Watt rotative beam engines, installed in 1858, and having previously been used on the South Devon Atmospheric Railway as blowing engines. All ceased work in 1924, being replaced by a 'Uniflow' plant, itself replaced by electric motors in 1969. For whatever reason I know not, this 'odd man out' was not cut up, and is beautifully looked after today. Observe the massive construction of the beam, timber lagged cylinder, valve chests and valve operating gear, and the operating levers for starting and stopping the engine, at platform level.*

46

47

46-47-48. At Crossness, on the south bank of the Thames, lies the largest concentration of beam engines in this country, four of triple expansion configuration, originally built in 1865, and laid out in cruciform. They are housed in a magnificent engine house, with a mass of decorative iron work, but most unfortunately, are in an extremely decrepit and woebegone condition today. Built by James Watt & Company, of the Soho Foundry, Birmingham, part of the large London Sewage Drainage Scheme, like the engines at West Ham (see Plates 57-8), in efforts to help prevent the multiplicity of separate discharges into the Thames. As built the engines were single cylinder, 48"x108", rotative machines, and Watt added surface condensers to improve their economy in 1885. To further increase the efficiency, in 1901, one at a time, the engines were converted to triple expansion, by adding new 'Corliss' valve cylinders, 19" high pressure, and 32" intermediate pressure, both with a 44" stroke. The existing cylinders then became the low pressure ones. New boilers working at 150 psi, being supplied at the same time. All this work was undertaken by Benjamin Goodfellow & Company, of Hyde. The engines stand today, looking extremely forlorn, and the condition of the building in which they are housed, boarders on dangerous, access being virtually impossible for safety reasons. The illustrations were taken on 6 November 1980, and they show: Plate 46, the beam platform, the beams themselves being 40' long; Plates 47-8, show the high and intermediate pressure cylinders with their valve gear - the low pressure cylinders are set at a lower level - and the auxiliary beam seen to the left of the intermediate cylinder in Plate 47, drives the condenser pumps. The fading splendour of the engine house is apparent in the last view. Replaced in 1945, the engines remained on stand-by until being last used in 1953. They originally carried names; 'Victoria', 'Prince Consort', 'Alexandra' and 'Albert Edward'. The Prince-of-Wales - later King Edward VII - 'started' them way back on 4 April 1865.

48.

49-50. *Cresswell Pumping Station of the Staffordshire Potteries Water Board, was the last station built by that undertaking, being commissioned in 1932. My photographs, taken on 15 June 1971, show the twin inverted triple expansion engines, built by Hawthorn Davey & Company Limited, and among the last engines to emerge from their Leeds works. The plant pumped from two new boreholes, and each engine had a deep bore hole pump, and a high lift pump, situated beneath the engines and driven by connecting rods from each crosshead. These engines were comparatively small by comparison with other pumping engines of similar configuration, but they were a neat design, extremely well kept, and painted maroon. They stopped work in 1976 and 1977, as electricity took over, and were scrapped shortly afterwards.*

51. *One of the few surviving, in its original location, 'grasshopper' beam engines; so named because the design of the beam, pivoted at one end rather than in the centre, gave the impression of such an insect when working. This engine was built by Andrew Barclay Sons & Company Limited, of Kilmarnock, a company better known for its industrial steam shunting locomotives, rather than stationary engines. The engine is a compound, notice the two cylinders side by side, dimensions being 36"x120", and 55"x156", is none rotative, and installed at Shore Road, Birkenhead, to drain the Mersey Railway tunnel. Originally built for the Mersey Railway, the engine eventually passed to the London Midland & Scottish Railway, and is currently in the ownership of British Railways. Although it passed out of use in 1959, the station is still used to house the electrical equipment for the present day pumps. The engine used to pump at between 4 and 7 strokes per minute, lifting 800 gallons per stroke, and the pump rods can be seen to the right of the picture, which was taken on 1 March 1979. The engine is fitted with 'Watts' parallel motion, a novel design of rods, intended to keep the piston rod parallel in the cylinder, without the use of slide bars and a crosshead; quite a simple idea, of which its designer was justifiably proud.*

52-53-54. *Addington Pumping Station, of the Croydon Water Authority, had two compound 'A' frame 'Woolf' beam engines, of almost identical design, except they were 'handed', and from different builders. Plate 52 shows the No 1, north, engine, the older of the two, built in 1888 by Easton & Anderson of Erith, with cylinders 20" and 34" diameter, with a 72" stroke. Its sister, shown in the other two illustrations, was built by Glenfield & Company Limited of Kilmarnock (later Glenfield & Kennedy), in 1893, to the same dimensions. Each engine had two pumps, both 19"x72", one driven from a downward extension of the low pressure piston rods, for the force pumps, delivering water to the reservoir; the others, driven from the beams, were the 205' deep bore hole pumps. Notice on Plate 52, the pump rods lying against the beam pivot, having been disconnected from the beam itself. The engines could each lift and deliver 1 500 000 gallons in 24 hours, running at 15 rpm, and they finished work in 1975. There were five 'Lancashire' boilers, two being in steam per engine, and the engine house crane, was driven by a single cylinder vertical engine mounted on the wall, somewhat of a novelty at so late a date. Photographs taken on 11 August 1980. Notice the belt driven governor, eccentric driven valve gear, and barring slots in the flywheel. Very pleasant and well built self contained, rather than 'house built', beam engines.*

55. *Builders plate of the Easton & Anderson engine at Addington.*

56. *Builders plate of the Glenfield engine at Addington.*

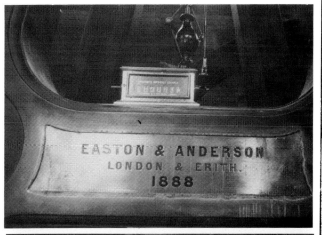

57

58.

57-58. The only remaining beam engines built by the Lilleshall Company of Oakengates, are these 1895-1900 built engines at West Ham Sewage Pumping Station. 'Woolf' compound rotative machines, similar in principle to the engines at Addington, but in this case 'house built'. The Cornish engineer Arthur Woolf, patented his design in 1803, that of placing two cylinders side by side at one end of the beam, which led to the two pistons having different strokes. In the case of these engines, the dimensions of the cylinders were 30"x57 11/16", and 48"x90"; this arrangement was popular, as it required little extra space. As at Addington, the bucket pumps, 5'2" diameter in this case, were two per engine, one driven off an extension of the high pressure piston rod, and the other off the beam, each had a stroke of 57 11/16", which was of course, the stroke of the beam, and they could lift a combined total of 1200 gallons per stroke of the engine, the normal running speed being 12 rpm. Notice the arrangement of 'Watts' parallel motion, the 'house built' staging around the engines, and the wood lagged cylinders. In plate 57, the No 1 engine of 1895 is on the right, and the No 2, 1900 built engine on the left. When I took the photographs on 6 November 1980, both were out of use, and had been since 1972, the No 2 engine being the last to run; it was stopped at 1200 noon precisely, on 10 January that year.

59. Makers plate on one of the engines at West Ham; despite one engine being built in 1895, both had 1900 plates.

60. An example of a small, simple, horizontal single cylinder none reversing engine, is this 1906 built machine by William Abell Limited, of Derby, a comparatively little known builder, at the works of the Derby Malt Vinegar Company Limited, in Derby. My photograph shows the engine on 28 August 1980, and still in use at that time. Notice the line shafting to the left, by which the engine drove the whole plant, as well as the arrangement of trunk guide and engine bed being integral with each other; the forged crankshaft is notable too. The cylinder was approximately 10"x18", and the working pressure, via an oil fired 'Cornish' boiler, 40 psi.

61. The name of Edwin Foden of Sandbach Cheshire, will forever be connected in most peoples minds with steam road traction, but in its early years the firm built a number of stationary steam engines, of all shapes and sizes. This photograph, taken on 21 August 1980, shows a small single cylinder, approximately 10"x18", reversing, link motion, slide valve winch engine, belonging to the British Waterways Board at Northwich - indeed not far from where it was built. The engine dated from the 1880s, and had been used to haul barges from the River Weaver onto a slipway. Fodens name was cast onto the slide valve cover, as well as the main bed, and when I visited this neat little engine, it had long been superseded. I could find no trace of the boiler plant, or indeed where it had been, and I fancy the engine may have been run off compressed air latterly. The replacement was an old tram traction motor, complete with controller, and this can be seen behind the cylinder of the Foden engine.

62. Another, apparently much older, Foden engine dating from around 1860, again a single cylinder, 12"x32", slide valve, in this case none reversing, and originally installed to drive a flour mill at Brereton, near Homes Chapel in Cheshire. The engine has a 'Porter' governor and jet condenser; note the very large flywheel. Before taking this photograph on 2 August 1980, my friend Paul Hulme and I, had to clear away a whole load of straw, as the engine house doubled up as a stable! The mill was primarily a water mill, and the engine had obviously been installed to assist the water wheel, which can just be seen through the opening to the right, when water was scarce; it was reputed to have last been so used, around the time of the First World War, and there was a clutch arrangement to facilitate this. The mill however, continued in use until just before the Second World War. There was a small 'Cornish' boiler the opposite side of the wall to the left, and the whole was an amazing survival, and well worth the trouble of finding.

63. Makers plate of the Foden engine at Brereton Mill.

65. William Boulton was a well known manufacturer of machinery in the Potteries, including steam engines, and here is one of his horizontal single cylinder machines, not dissimilar to the one in the previous illustration, and built in 1888 at his Burslem Works. The engine drove the blungers, where the clay was first processed, at the Burleigh Pottery of Burgess & Leigh Limited, in Middleport, and alongside the Trent & Mersey Canal. I took these photographs on 3 May 1980, and by that time the engine had been replaced by an electric motor, and the single coal fired 'Lancashire' boiler was cold. Notice the large flywheel, belt driven governor - belt missing - and similar arrangement of crosshead to the engine illustrated in Plate 64 - a very nice old, and elegant machine.

66. Builders plate of the engine in plate 65.

*64.  The use of small steam engines in the North Straffordshire pottery industry was once prolific, but by the 1980s few remained.  This is an interesting single cylinder, slide valve, horizontal engine, maker and date unknown, but said to have been over 100 years old, when this photographs was taken on 3 May 1980.  The engine drove the sliphouse, which was where the clay (slip) was prepared, at Dunn Bennett & Company Limited, Dalehall Works, Middleport, in Stoke-on-Trent, and without doubt would have been built locally, a number of Potteries engineering firms specialising in making small simple engines like this, for the industry.  Notice the type of slidebar, often used on engines that run in one direction only, where the main thrust was always in one direction.  The engine had a crankshaft governor, which can just be seen within the drum in front of the large flywheel.  This type of governor regulates the engine speed by moving the eccentric centre, relative to the centre of its driveshaft, and thus alters the travel of the valve, and hence cut-off.  The flywheel drove the machinery via a belt. A very neat engine, in clean surroundings.*

65.

66.

67. Some potteries and their associated industries used beam engines, especially in the early days, and this magnificent old single cylinder rotative engine, is at the Etruscan Bone Mill of Jesse Shirley & Sons Limited, at Etruria. The cylinder is 13"x60", giving a nominal 97 bhp, and the engine reputed to have been built by Sherratt of Salford, as far back as 1839; it was certainly installed at these works by them in 1858. However, later repairs were undertaken by the local firm of Kirk of Etruria, also famous for their beam engines. The mill is situated alongside the Trent & Mersey Canal, just on the Stoke side of the Summit Lock, and I well recall as a boy, watching with amazement from the opposite bank of the canal, the graceful beam 'nodding' up and down, as the engine worked. The boiler house with a 'Lancashire' boiler, abutted the canal, at a lower level, and the boiler backhead used to shine with the polished brasswork, the coal for it being delivered by canal boat. Although the engine finished work in 1972, this illustration was taken back in 1947. Notice the large flywheel, name plate 'Princess' on the wallside, gear driven governor, and part of the valve gear. The curvature of the nameplate led to the local legend that the engine had once powered a paddle steamer, but I find this extremely difficult to reconcile! Today the engine is beautifully preserved, and available for inspection.
(EJD Warrillow; courtesy Keele University Library)

68. The Derbyshire Silica Firebrick Company Limited, used this Robey horizontal duplex engine, to drive part of their works at Hartington, in Derbyshire, photographed on 8 April 1980. The engine was said to have come from a Staffordshire colliery some 60 years earlier, and had been built in 1902, the makers numbers being: right hand No 22111, and left hand No 22110. Notice the multi flat belt drive, the engine having conventional slide valves. Unfortunately, it had finished work a few months before I visited, but had in any event, only been used intermittently for some years earlier.